Bread FOR THE Winter

Harvey Yoder

ISBN: 978-1-936208-13-5

Illustrations by Igor Kondratyuk
Cover design and layout: Lydia Zook

Second printing: November 2013
Printed in the USA

Published by:
TGS International
P.O. Box 355 · Berlin, Ohio 44610 USA
Phone: 330-893-4828
Fax: 330-893-2305
www.tgsinternational.com

TGS000732

CHAPTER ONE
Papa's Story

In the country of Ukraine, a small village lies on the vast, fertile plain that stretches for miles in all directions. This village is not nearly as old as many other towns in Ukraine, for it is not even a hundred years old. In fact, it was just six years old in 1936, at the time this story happened. It had only twenty-nine houses built along the sides of the single dirt street that passed through it.

The houses were all built with brick and mud, and had steep straw roofs to shed as much of the rain as possible. Even though they were small, these houses were much better than the dark, damp dugouts where the villagers had lived when they had first arrived in this place. That first winter many families had lived together in a few dugout houses with sod chunks for walls and a tarp for a roof. As soon as they were able, each family had built a mud brick home so they could move up out of the earth.

But Pavel had no memory of all that. He had been only two years old when he and his parents had moved to Ukraine. For Pavel, this was now the very best place he could ever imagine. In the summer the sunshine was warm and pleasant on the gardens and fields. It brought life and nourishment to the fruits and vegetables, and especially to the fields of wheat.

In the winter the snow came and the cold winds blew around the corners of the house. The chill reached into the tiniest cracks and sent Pavel huddling close to the big clay cook stove that kept their small house warm and cozy. When the wind blew especially cold, Pavel liked to sleep on a shelf that had been built over part of the stove.

But on this summer day there was no cold or snow. Pavel was working with Papa and Mama in their wheat field. He was carefully helping Mama gather the cut stalks of wheat so they could be carried into the barn.

"Pavel, it is good that you are growing stronger every year," Papa said.

Pavel stood up as tall as his eight years would let him. *"Da,"* he said, using the Russian word for *yes.* "Look at this!" He pushed his shirt sleeve up above his elbow and flexed his arm. When his muscle made a little bulge under his skin, Pavel laughed.

"Ah, it is that good bread Mama makes from the wheat," Papa said. "To see you grow strong and healthy is such a good gift from God. Maria, is it not so?"

Maria was the name other people used for his mama. Pavel never used it though, for it did not sound nearly as nice as *Mama.* The name *Mama* had such a warm, comforting feeling. It was like the feeling he always got when his mother knelt beside him to pray before he crawled into his bed at night.

"Da, Alexander, it is good to see our son growing so big," Mama replied quietly. She smiled at her husband before bending over to gather more wheat stalks.

"We serve such a good God," Papa said as he rested the scythe on the ground. He leaned on the handle, careful to point the sharp blade away from him. "In the old country, back in Belarus (bee lah ROOS), we never had such wheat as this." His eyes went to the garden that lay between the wheat field and their house. "We never had such a wonderful garden of vegetables either. *Da*, we are truly blessed by our good God."

A small cloud seemed to have passed over the sun for a moment. It was always like that when Pavel heard about the old country of Belarus. He had heard that it was mostly forested and cold and rainy and snowy. That is what Papa had told Pavel. Of course, there must have been some happy memories from the land of Pavel's birth, but everyone seemed to remember only the hardships they had known back then.

"We had no such wheat fields in Belarus, did we, Papa?" Pavel asked, digging his sun-tanned toes into the black soil.

Papa looked out across the fields that stretched to the west. "We had some wheat, but the ground was full of roots and the wheat did not grow well in the poor soil. Every year we cleared more trees so we could grow more wheat, but each year the harvest was barely enough to feed us."

"And now we have grown beautiful wheat here for the past six years," Mama added, standing up and rubbing her back. "I think God has given us more every year."

Papa looked at Mama and a big smile spread across his entire face. "*Da, Maria,*" he said gratefully. For a moment he bowed his head and closed his eyes.

Pavel bent over and continued gathering the wheat stalks into bundles. This made it easier for Mama to pile the wheat stalks on the cart that was pulled by their horse, Big Red. When Papa opened his eyes and took the scythe in his strong hands once more, he smiled and winked at Pavel.

Pavel giggled and ducked his head. He knew what Papa had been doing. Papa had been thanking God when he closed his eyes and bowed his head. He did that a lot.

All afternoon the three worked together. Papa swung the

big scythe and the ripe wheat fell in neat rows. Pavel followed him and gathered the wheat into bundles. Mama collected the bundles and stacked them in neat rows on the cart. Then she clucked to Big Red. The horse walked carefully forward until Mama called "B-r-r-r," rolling the *r*'s. That was how they told a horse to stop in Russian.

They had spoken the Russian language in Belarus, and they spoke Russian here in Ukraine. Papa had explained to Pavel that the country of Russia had conquered both Belarus and Ukraine. That was why everyone was required to learn Russian. In school it was the only language the students were permitted to use.

Although Pavel grew hot and sweaty, he did not stop working during that whole afternoon. Why would he stop? He was helping to bring in the harvest and he knew the harvest was important. The harvest meant food, both for now and for the winter when the snow would lie heavy and white on the land.

"There. It is all cut," Papa called after making the last sweep with the scythe. His weary voice sounded relieved and happy.

Pavel looked at Papa and laughed. "The big field is finished," he called joyfully across the neat rows of grain. "The wheat is all cut!"

Mama put another bundle of cut wheat on the cart. She had to stand on her tiptoes to reach high enough to stack it on the big load. Then she, too, looked at Papa and smiled. "What a good feeling!" she breathed.

"Maria, you must stop now," Papa said as he walked toward Mama. "You have worked enough for today. We will take the loaded cart to the barn now. While I milk the cow and Pavel gets the eggs, you will rest just a few minutes before we eat our supper." He placed his hand on Mama's shoulder and looked kindly into her eyes. "Are you feeling well?" he asked gently.

It was always like that—Papa making sure that Mama did not work too hard. "She is a hard worker and does not know when to stop," Papa sometimes told Pavel's uncles and aunts. "I must not forget to watch out for her and tell her when to rest."

Now Mama said, "Oh, yes, Alexander. I am feeling quite well. When we all work together to bring in the harvest, I feel like I have new energy. Just think how wonderful it is to have such a harvest. We must be so thankful to our God."

Papa nodded. Then he looked toward the setting sun. "I do not think we need to worry about rain," he said. "We will leave the rest of the wheat in the field. Tomorrow, after the sun has dried the dew off the wheat, we can gather the rest."

Pavel was happy to hear that. All afternoon he had wanted to know if they would work late into the night to get all the wheat into the barn, but he had not asked. He thought it might sound too much as though he was tired. He did not want his parents to think that he was weak. He was determined to help bring in the harvest.

Pavel enjoyed every bite of his supper. He ate fresh tomatoes and cucumbers from the garden, a vegetable soup they called borscht, and thick slices of bread baked in the clay oven. Afterward Pavel sat beside Papa on the wooden bench under the grape arbor. "Papa," he said, as he always did after supper, "please tell me a story."

The stories Papa told were even better than the stories from the few books that Pavel had read. There were only a handful of books in the village and Pavel had already read most of them. Those treasured books were passed from house to house. Everyone was very careful to keep them clean and treat them as gently as if they were alive.

"Tell about the trip to Ukraine," Pavel now suggested. "Tell about the time when I was still a baby."

Papa motioned for Mama to sit beside him. "Maria, let's rest now," he invited.

Mama smiled and nodded agreeably. She sat down and folded her hands in her lap with a tired but happy sigh. Her face looked peaceful in the summer twilight.

"I will tell you about the time before we moved here to Ukraine," Papa said, smoothing Pavel's hair. "It is important that you know about your heritage."

Pavel nodded, but suddenly the evening seemed even darker than it was. He wished he didn't have to hear that story, but he said nothing.

"In Belarus, we men worked hard from morning until night trying to make a living for our families," Papa began. "We chopped down trees and pulled the roots from the stubborn soil. We planted our seeds, and we fertilized the plants with manure to help them grow. But in the thin sunshine, they grew very poorly. We planted the potatoes and watched as the first green shoots came up out of the ground. We kept daily watch for the bugs and picked them off the plants."

Papa's voice paused. In the darkness Pavel heard the sound of crickets chirping. He heard Big Red making chomping sounds in the barn. One of his cousins laughed somewhere down the street.

"Sometimes," Papa continued, "the sun did not shine for days and our gardens did not grow. The wheat looked yellow and only grew this high." Papa dropped his hand below his knee to show Pavel how poorly the wheat grew.

"We prayed and sometimes we got good crops, although most of the time we hardly had enough to eat. Then," Papa stopped and cleared his throat, "we had three bad summers in a row. We knew we had to do something to care for our families. All the believers got together one evening to pray and ask God what we should do to feed our children."

Pavel thought about the good food he had eaten for supper. He especially remembered the bread. The bread made from the wheat they grew in the fields every year.

"We had no bread." The dreaded words came from Papa's mouth. Pavel knew they were coming, but he held his breath like he always did when Papa said those words.

No bread? How could anyone live without bread? Pavel could not imagine life without bread. He ate bread every day. In fact, he ate it with every meal. In the morning his family ate sliced bread with *kasha,* their hot breakfast cereal. When they had the rare treat of fried eggs, once again they had bread. At lunchtime they had bread along with hot potatoes or borscht or salad. In the evening they ate bread once more with the leftovers from lunch or with anything else Mama put on the table. Pavel simply could not imagine a meal without bread.

"So, for one more winter, there was no wheat to make bread," Papa continued. "We talked to God and asked Him what to do."

"And that is when Uncle Yuri and Uncle Veniyamin (veh nee

yah MEEN) came here," Pavel interrupted excitedly. He liked this part of the story. He called both men uncle, even though only Yuri was his real uncle. True, Veniyamin was also related to his papa, but he was not his brother like Yuri was. But it was always polite to call any older men in the village by the respectful title of uncle. All the women were called aunt too.

"Yuri and Veniyamin were sent out on the train after we had all gathered together to pray for them. Someone had told us that there were jobs in the coal mines at Donetsk (dohn YEHTSK), so the two men bought tickets to travel to Donetsk."

Pavel could not imagine how exciting it must have been for the uncles to ride on the train. Many times Pavel had seen the train pass close by their village, just at the end of the street. It never stopped there, because there was no train station. Sometimes he could see people looking out the windows as the train rumbled past. He often thought about Yuri and Veniyamin, heading toward Donetsk but never getting there.

Papa nodded, as though reading his son's mind. "*Da*, they traveled for a long, long time. Finally, just up the track from here, at the station in Hopa, the train stopped and the two men stepped off. The train was to stop for a long time, and they were happy for a chance to walk about after the long ride from Belarus."

Yes, the stop in Hopa. Pavel knew that stop was an important part of the story.

"They saw a man who was waiting to give people a ride in his taxi, so they started to talk to him. They were delighted to discover that he was a believer! They had quickly found a Christian man, so far away from their home!" Papa's voice rose with excitement as he recounted the story. "They told the man that they were from Belarus and that they were going to Donetsk to look for jobs in the coal mines. They explained that they were sent by the prayers of the people from home."

Pavel always loved this part of the story, but the day of harvesting had been long and hot. Now he could not keep his head from nodding sleepily against Papa's side.

"Uh-oh," Papa chuckled gently. "The boy is going to sleep already." He smiled at Mama.

"Tell me more," Pavel begged, sitting up straight and looking into Papa's shadowy face. "I want to hear the good part."

"The next part will have to wait," Papa smiled, and Pavel knew it would do no good to beg. "*Da*, Papa," he said obediently. He covered his mouth as a huge yawn came out.

But Pavel was still awake as he knelt with Mama on the floor beside his bed. Together they prayed to God. As he always did, Pavel thanked God for bringing them here to Brothers' Village. It was called that because all the people in the village were Christian brothers and sisters.

Pavel also remembered to thank God for the wheat and the bread. Especially the bread. With another yawn, he dropped wearily into his bed. Before Mama could even go out the door into the front room, he was asleep.

The moon rose gently and began its slow journey across the sky, shining its mellow light into Brothers' Village in Ukraine. The day seemed to end with a sigh of satisfaction as it sank restfully into the arms of the night.

CHAPTER TWO

Surprise for Mama

"Cock-a-doodle to you," Pavel said with a giggle to the big white rooster. Then he hurried to finish pouring water into the chickens' bowl. Already the morning sun was shining warmly, and Pavel heard Papa bring Big Red out of his stall. The harness jingled as their horse was hitched to the empty cart. Papa had earlier stacked the wheat in the barn while he was waiting for the cut wheat in the field to dry.

"Today the men will finish the harvest," Papa said when Pavel had finished his chores. "Maria, I heard that Aunt Natasha is in need of help with her work. I thought maybe you would like to help her today."

"Certainly," Mama agreed. "She is in need of help with all her little ones."

Uncle Vanya and Aunt Natasha had seven children. The oldest boy was about the same age as Pavel. There was always extra work to do for a family of that size, and Pavel's parents often helped them.

"*Da*, Papa, we men can finish the wheat harvest," Pavel said stoutly.

Papa's eyes twinkled. He felt the muscles on Pavel's arm. Nodding gravely, he repeated, "We men." Papa and Pavel laughed together.

All morning Pavel carried the cut bundles of wheat to Papa. He watched as Papa carefully loaded the wheat onto the cart. Then he signaled to Big Red to move forward and stopped him by calling "B-r-r-r" just as Mama had done the day before.

When the cart was full, they walked beside the load while Papa guided Big Red into the barn. The bundles of wheat from the day before were neatly stacked along one wall.

Pavel watched as Papa began a new stack. First he placed several boards on the hard dirt floor. Then he laid a layer of wheat stalks all across the boards, letting the heads hang out over the front. He stacked the second layer in the other direction, making the stack stronger, and now the heads hung out on the right side. The third layer was turned to the back, and the fourth layer hung over the left side.

As Papa continued stacking the bundles, he turned each layer. That way the heads hung free and could dry out completely. One more load and the harvest was in. Before Papa could stack the final load, the yard gate opened. A moment later Pavel heard Uncle Vladik calling, "Good morning!"

"Good morning," Papa replied and smiled a welcome.

"It's been another good year for wheat," Uncle Vladik said, nodding at the stacked piles of wheat.

"How good God has been to us once more!" Papa exclaimed, following their visitor's glance.

"Is Sasha with you, Uncle?" Pavel asked Uncle Vladik. He hoped to hear that his cousin and best friend had come too.

"No, Pavlik," Uncle Vladik said, using Pavel's affectionate nickname. "Sasha is helping his brothers and sisters in the vegetable garden. No," he repeated, looking soberly at Papa, "I have come to tell you the latest about our government."

"What is it now?" Papa asked seriously.

"The new tax laws are being passed," Uncle Vladik replied. "The taxes are much higher than ever before. The communist workers are being sent out to tax the harvest of every village."

Pavel could hear the two men talking, but he didn't pay close attention. He had been hearing the grownups talk a lot about the changes in the government. Mostly it had not seemed very important to him. While the men talked, he sat on the floor and played with the kittens that had just come out of a hole in the straw a week before. He took a piece of straw and slowly passed it in front of a spotted kitten. The kitten watched the moving straw and suddenly pounced on it. It scratched at the stalk with its tiny claws. Pavel laughed and wiggled the straw again.

When he heard Papa and Uncle Vladik begin to pray, Pavel quickly stood up. He bowed his head respectfully as the men were doing.

"You are the same God who brought us here to Ukraine from our old home in Belarus," Papa prayed. "You took care of us all during the journey and in the good years since then. We know you will continue to care for us in these troubling times. We will not doubt you now. You have proved yourself faithful, Lord, in all the times we have called upon you."

It was always the same. Papa never forgot to thank God for what He had done for them before he asked for anything. Pavel remembered that Papa had told him how much God loved it when His children were thankful.

"It is what God is waiting to hear," Papa had said. "His ears are turned toward His children. He waits to hear our praise and thanksgiving."

Now, as he listened to the men praying, Pavel felt sure that God would care for them. After all, He had cared for them as long as Pavel could remember.

Finally Uncle Vladik left. For a moment Papa stood still, staring thoughtfully at his shoes. When he saw Pavel watching him, Papa smiled. "Now," he said, "if we can get the last load off the cart, we will have time to finish the table. Mama will be surprised if the table is done when she comes home."

Pavel nodded and smiled. He had watched Papa's skillful hands shape the table from rough lumber. He had watched the legs being carved last winter as the family sat around the stove. Now the boards for the top had been smoothed and the table was almost done.

"*Da*, Mama will like the table," Pavel said. "It will be much stronger than our old one."

Papa chuckled. "No more tumbling-down table when Uncle Yuri leans too heavily on it." They both laughed as they remembered the loose boards crashing down on the floor during a visit from the relatives.

As Papa was fastening the boards to the table frame, Pavel remembered the unfinished story. "Papa," he said, "now you can finish telling me the story of how Brothers' Village was started."

"Oh, the waiting is to be over?" Papa teased. He laid another board across the frame of the table. Cranking a hand drill, he began carefully boring a hole through the board.

Pavel waited until the hole was finished before he replied. "*Da*. Tell how the taxi man brought Uncle Yuri and Uncle Veniyamin to this very place."

Papa pushed the sharp plane across a rough part of the

board. He rubbed the wood with his hand, checking whether it was smooth enough. Then he continued to plane thin shavings from the board.

"Well, you see," he began, "the taxi man asked them, 'Why go to Donetsk to mine the coal if you are farmers? There is good land here. The soil is rich and black and grows wonderful wheat and vegetables. The government wants this land to be farmed and will give each family a small plot. You should ask God about settling here and farming this land.' "

Rubbing his hand over the smooth board, Papa continued, "The taxi man invited them to come see this land where we now live. It was good, just like he had said. When the uncles finally got back to the train station, they found that the train had already left for Donetsk!"

Papa stopped the story while he drilled another hole. Then he continued, "The taxi man said that might have been a sign from God. He advised them to pray about moving here instead. When the uncles prayed, they felt the blessing of God on this man's words. So instead of going on to Donetsk, they returned to Belarus and told us about this amazing happening.

"We all gathered together to pray and ask God if this was the place where we should move to. In the end everyone felt that God was sending us here. Twenty-nine families prepared to make the long move from Belarus to Ukraine. We brought only the most necessary items, for we did not have money to travel on the trains. We made wooden sleds and piled our few belongings on them. Those who had horses hitched them to those sleds, but some people had to pull theirs by hand."

Pavel looked at Big Red standing patiently in his stall. He

tried to imagine their horse walking all that distance, pulling a heavy sled. He pictured Papa and Mama, along with the uncles and aunts and children, walking that great distance. He imagined the camps they made, and how they rested along the way to let the people and horses keep their strength.

The drill bit into the wood again, creating another smooth hole. Papa continued, "Then one day, after two months of travel, we finally arrived here. We felt like the children of Israel arriving in the land of Canaan. We were so grateful to God for bringing us here that the first thing we did was build the small house of prayer. It was so tiny that only six people could fit inside at one time. During those first days, it was never empty as we took turns to go in and thank God for His kindness in bringing us here. You have seen that house of prayer, Pavel, for it still stands at the edge of the village."

"*Da,* Papa," Pavel said. He had the same feeling of awe that he often felt in church. It was a good feeling that made Pavel know God was with them.

"We had to hurry and dig our dugouts before the winter came," Papa continued. "Some of the men went to other villages to find work. They brought back vegetables as pay, and we stored them underground too. That first winter was hard for us, but we were thankful that it was not as cold and long as winters in Belarus. How we rejoiced when spring came and we began to prepare the land for planting."

While he talked, Papa placed the last board on the table top. He drilled the final holes, fastened the board, and the table was done. "Just like this table is now finished, so the story is finished for now," Papa laughed. "Come, Pavel, help me carry it into the house. We will put it in the big room and surprise your mother!"

Pavel was excited as he helped his father carry the wooden table into the big front room that they used for church services on Sundays. When the table was neatly placed in the middle of the room, they stood back and admired it.

"Wait, Papa," Pavel said suddenly and ran outside. He quickly picked some lacy white flowers from beside the road and ran back to the kitchen. He carefully placed the flowers in a small jar and set them in the center of the new table.

"Just the right thing, Pavel," Papa said, looking admiringly at the bouquet. "That is just what was needed to make our new table look beautiful."

Just then they heard the click of the yard gate as Mama arrived.

"Surprise!" Pavel shouted as Mama walked into the room. He jumped around on one foot in his excitement. "Surprise, Mama!"

Mama's eyes grew wide and she exclaimed, "Oh, how beautiful!" She rubbed her hand admiringly over the smooth wood. Then she turned to Papa and said, "Thank you, Alexander!"

Papa smiled and replied, "You are welcome. I am happy that you will finally have a strong table to work the dough when you make bread. And see, Pavel has picked some flowers for your new table."

"I see," Mama said, smiling at her son. "My men have done more than just finish the harvest today."

That evening when Mama knelt beside Pavel to pray, she thanked God for her new table. She also thanked Him for the wheat harvest that was in the barn. Then there was a little silence.

Pavel could hear Papa in the next room reading aloud from his Bible as he did each evening. At Pavel's bedside, Mama continued praying quietly. "God," she said, "I will not worry about the taxes. I will trust in you. Thank you, Jesus."

Pavel wanted to ask about the taxes, but it made him feel nervous. So he stayed silent. Somehow he was feeling the same way he always did when Papa talked about Belarus. Why did the fear buzz around in his head like a fly?

Mama rested her hand briefly on Pavel's forehead, and his fear went away. He shifted into a comfortable position on the bed and watched as she left his little room to join Papa. Their low voices continued in prayer and reading.

It was good that the wheat harvest was in. Pavel felt satis-fied and happy as he fell asleep thinking about all that good wheat in the barn. That night small clouds begin to gather over Brothers' Village. They darkened the moon that was still making its way across the night sky. Soon the autumn rains would come.

CHAPTER THREE
Clouds of Fear

"Good-bye, good-bye! God go with you and bless you as you travel!" Papa called. Pavel stood between his parents and his cousins, waving at the farm wagon as it rolled away.

The wagon was not loaded with hay or potatoes this time. Instead, it had a load of people on it, including Uncle Vladik and Aunt Nadya. They were going to share the Good News of Jesus in other villages. All of Uncle Vladik's children except the baby were staying behind at Pavel's house.

Sasha was standing beside Pavel and beyond him were the rest of the cousins. Larissa and Masha, often mistaken for twins, were there. Next came Andrei, and then Mikhail, whom everyone called Misha. And still there were more children: Peter and Victor and two-year-old Tanya. Tanya was in Mama's arms, happily chewing on a dry piece of bread.

"Okay," Papa said cheerfully as the wagon disappeared in the distance. He smiled at all the cousins who would be staying with them for the next month. "So many helpers will make it easy to prepare the garden for winter. Pavel, you and the big boys bring out rakes while I take the little ones with me to the garden."

Pavel and the big boys ran down to the storage shed and collected the rakes. There were not enough rakes for each boy to have one, but that was fine. They would all be busy as some of them raked and others carried away the dried cucumber and bean stalks.

The garden was much busier than when Pavel and his parents worked alone. Having so many cousins to help was great fun. They raked and gathered vines into piles and burned them. "The fire will burn any insect eggs that were laid on the vines," Papa said as the gray smoke rose slowly from the piles. "That way they can't hatch into bugs that would eat our plants next year."

When the work was finished, they all enjoyed the big pot of borscht that Mama had prepared for their lunch. The thick slices of crusty bread also disappeared rapidly as they ate around the new table.

"The food is vanishing faster than snow in the sunshine," Papa laughed as the children hungrily ate every bite of the borscht. "Praise God that we have plenty of food."

"Thank you for the food, Uncle and Aunt. It was very good," Sasha said respectfully when he had finished eating. There was a polite chorus of agreement from the rest of the children, for they had all been taught good manners.

"It is the Lord who has blessed us with good food," Papa replied. Everyone stood around the table as they thanked God for the meal they had eaten.

"While the younger ones take their naps," Papa said afterward, "we will go to the cousins' garden and work there. We are going to stay very busy taking care of both places while the preaching group is gone."

All afternoon Pavel and his cousins worked hard. By evening everyone was tired from the day of raking and gathering dry stalks. When the eggs were all gathered, the cow milked, and the chickens fed, the children all ate together in Pavel's home. After supper the entire group went to the cousins' house to sleep where they had more beds.

Mama was washing the little children's hands and faces. Papa was helping the older ones get ready for bed. Pavel was preparing the bed he would share with Sasha and Andrei and Misha. The bed would be very full, but there was enough space for all four of them. Before they got into bed, Pavel heard a voice outside in the dusk calling for Papa.

Papa went out the door and into the street. After a few minutes he came in again looking very sober. He nodded gently at Mama, and they both looked at the four boys preparing for bed. "There are more reports of the tax people taking goods from the villages," Papa said gravely and yet calmly. "The brothers are asking the people to pray to God. We need Him to show us how to accept this new law as Christians should."

Pavel looked deeply into Papa's eyes. He saw the same quiet look of peace that Papa always had.

"Will they take away our food?" Sasha asked fearfully.

"They are taking away food from many of the villages," Papa replied truthfully. "However, some people have reported that the tax collectors do leave a little food behind."

The room was very quiet. Tanya slept peacefully in Mama's arms.

"We will pray," Papa said finally, and everyone knelt in a circle.

It was hard for Pavel to pay attention as Papa prayed. His mind raced in scary circles. He thought about Belarus, and the familiar cloud of fear hovered over his thoughts. Even when Mama prayed, Pavel's mind felt dark and fearful.

He pictured the golden stacks of wheat in the barn. Surely the tax collectors wouldn't take away their wheat! Pavel thought about the flour that Papa brought home after taking bags of wheat to the mill. He could almost taste the crusty, golden bread that Mama baked in the clay oven.

If all their wheat was taken away, what would they eat? Would the tax people try to take the cabbages and carrots that were still in the garden? Would they come again and take those vegetables after they were harvested? The endless questions had no answers.

It was his turn to pray, but Pavel had nothing to say. His cousins prayed, and then all four boys went to bed. One by one, his cousins fell asleep. All was still in the bedroom, but Pavel could not sleep. His mind was too busy thinking. He tried to roll over in the bed, but there was not enough room. The bed creaked as he settled back on his side.

"Pavlik?" The gentle voice in the darkness was Mama's.

Pavel sat up. He slipped softly from the bed and went to his mother.

"Come," Mama whispered kindly, and they went into the big room together. Pavel could see Papa sitting quietly beside a dim lamp.

"You are not sleeping?" Papa asked. "Too much thinking?"

Pavel nodded his head silently. Papa motioned for Pavel to come and snuggle on his lap.

"When we first came here to Brothers' Village, God blessed us with more each year. Life was good and we were not hungry like we had been in Belarus," Papa said in a low voice that would not wake up the cousins. "Oh, how we thanked God for His blessings as we saw the wheat and vegetables growing in the beautiful sunshine. The rains came just when they were needed. Every day we thanked God for bringing us into this land of plenty. Our village was a pleasant place to live. On Sundays everyone gathered to praise God together. There was no stealing and we lived together in peace the way God wants His children to live.

"But God reminded us that He expected us to share our blessings. We began to pray, Pavel, and God showed us something important. It is something that you need to understand also."

Papa's chest felt warm and comforting as Pavel rested against him and listened to the low rumble of his father's voice. "Before Jesus went to heaven, He told His disciples that they were to go into all the world and tell others the Good News of salvation. They were to stay in Jerusalem until they were filled with the Holy Spirit. After that, they were to preach about Jesus to all the people who had not heard of Him. You've heard me read that from the book of Acts in the Bible. Well, that is the story of how the believers went around telling everyone about Jesus. They proclaimed that He was the Messiah who had come into the world to save sinners."

Pavel thought about the Bible that Papa read from. It was one of only three Bibles in Brothers' Village, so it was a precious treasure.

Papa's voice continued, "We felt that God was speaking to us about taking the Gospel to others. We thought, *All the people in our village are believers. What other people need to hear the Good News?* And so we continued to pray."

Papa's voice sounded as if he had forgotten that he was talking to Pavel. He went on thoughtfully, "God seemed to be reminding us of the many nearby villages that had not heard the truth about Jesus. There were churches in some of these villages, but they taught the ideas and traditions of men instead of the Word of God. We felt we had to share Jesus with those people.

"I was on that first wagon trip with three other brothers. We hitched the horses to a farm wagon and set out, not knowing where we would go or how long we would stay. We only knew that the Spirit of God would show us the way."

It was easy for Pavel to picture that first group, for it had been much like the one that had set out only that morning. After the men made the first few trips, the women had started to go along too.

"We can sing," the men had said, "but the singing is much better when we have the women to help us. We also believe that God wants the women to speak with the women in the villages. Everyone needs to hear the Gospel."

Now Papa continued, "We went to the first village and asked the people if we could stay for the night. It was warm, and we camped out under the wagon. Before we slept, we began to sing songs of praise. When the people heard our songs, they came out and listened. More than a hundred people gathered quickly that evening."

Pavel nodded his head. He knew it was like that even in their village. If anything interesting was happening, it did not take long for the whole village to get together.

"That night we began to tell the people about salvation in Jesus. They listened until late in the night, and some of them asked if they could hear even more. We prayed and felt that God wanted us to stay there a few more days. The people gave us food, and some of them returned the next day to ask questions. That evening there was an even bigger crowd."

It was a good story, but the day had been long and Pavel had worked hard. His eyelids began to droop.

"That was just the beginning of our trips to the villages around here," Papa said. "Of course, we have not been welcomed in all the villages. In some places there are people who are angry that we keep coming back. But by God's grace, there are now believers in many of the villages where we have preached. We want to encourage them and help them as much as we can."

Pavel nodded sleepily. He thought of the wagonload of people who had left that morning. He could picture them sharing the Good News in the villages. He hoped that soon he would be big enough to go along on those trips. He wanted to tell people about Jesus too.

Mama drew him gently from Papa's lap and guided him back to bed. As Pavel lay down beside his sleeping cousins, his mind was at rest. He could not even remember the scary thoughts that had kept him awake, and he quickly fell asleep.

CHAPTER FOUR
Heavenly Music

Pavel was walking home from school by himself at the end of a day of lessons. He had stayed after school so he could finish copying a song he wanted to take home for Mama. That was the way the villagers got copies of songs and sermons and even the Bible. Someone had to make a copy by hand, usually from someone else's copy. Then they shared their handwritten manuscripts with others who wished to read the song or sermon or portion of the Bible.

> *Your voice, O Lord, is the voice I want to hear.*
> *Your will, O Lord, is the will of my heart.*
> *Only yours, Lord, only yours.*

Pavel tried to memorize the words as he walked along the road. He knew Mama would sing the words, but he wanted to know the song by memory so he could sing along with her. He thought about the words of the song and wondered what it would be like to hear the voice of God. He remembered stories that Papa read from the Bible about people who heard God speak.

Pavel began to make up a tune and sing the words to himself. "Your voice, O Lord, is the voice I want to hear." Over and over he sang the line, making his own melody.

When he stopped singing for a moment, Pavel heard something unusual. It sounded like music. He stopped walking and listened some more. Somewhere, not very far away, people were singing. It was not very loud, yet he could distinctly hear the sound of a beautiful song. Never in his life had Pavel heard such music!

For a moment Pavel closed his eyes and let the melody ring in his ears. He had never imagined that even the angels could sing so wonderfully. It seemed to Pavel that the music was moving. At first he heard it somewhere above him and then beyond the houses and across the railroad track.

What he was hearing with his ears seemed to spread down into the very center of his being. Opening his eyes, he looked around. He was just beyond Sasha's house, so he ran back to get his cousins.

"Sasha! Misha! Come! Listen, there is music!" Pavel burst into his cousins' house and beckoned to them with his hand.

The boys rushed out. Music? On a Friday?

They followed Pavel to the street where they stopped and listened.

A gentle breeze blew through the waiting boys' hair. A hen cackled in someone's barn. The voice of a woman calling to her child came from somewhere down the street.

"It's gone," Pavel said in great disappointment. "I really, truly heard it and I wanted you to hear it too."

"What did it sound like?" Sasha asked, and Pavel knew that at least his cousin believed him.

"It was so beautiful," Pavel said with a sigh. "Never have I heard such beautiful singing in my life."

"Could it have come from another village?" Misha asked.

Pavel shook his head. No, there would be no such music coming from another village. And this music had moved around to different places and had seemed to come from the sky. Pavel left his cousins and hurried home.

He wanted to tell Papa and Mama about the singing he had heard, but it did not seem to be the right time. There was work to be done. Mama had been waiting for Pavel to take the cow out to graze. When he gave her the song he had copied, she said that it would have to wait until later.

There were a few other children watching their cows too. The village had only about ten cows for nearly thirty families. Having a cow was a special responsibility in the village. Papa had bought this cow only a year before, but she provided plenty of milk. When the calf was born in the spring, there had been enough milk for them to share with many other families. One time Mama had even managed to save some cream to make butter. Pavel had taken his turn with the churn and had helped to make some delicious butter to spread on their bread. What a treat that had been! Pavel smacked his lips at the memory.

When Pavel brought the cow home that evening so Mama could milk her, he was surprised to see a group of men in the yard. He was puzzled when he saw them go into the big room in their house where the church services were held on Sundays.

The frightening thoughts barged into Pavel's mind again. Were the tax collectors coming? Was the wheat in the barn going to be seized? Would they have bread for the winter?

Finally the cow was milked and the men left the house. The family sat down to eat their borscht and bread. The sun was already down and the last light of day shone over the village. Papa said very little during the supper. As soon as it was over, he went out and sat on the bench. Pavel and Mama soon joined him.

Suddenly Pavel remembered the singing he had heard that afternoon. Eagerly he told his parents about it. "It was so beautiful," he said with a wistful sigh. "I wish you could have heard it too."

Mama looked at Papa and they both looked at their son.

"What do you think it was?" Pavel inquired, looking up at his parents' faces.

"I think you heard the heavenly chorus of angels," Papa said thoughtfully after a few moments.

Pavel nodded. He had concluded the same thing that afternoon while he was watching the cow and pondering.

"Pavel, you have been blessed with God's favor many times," Mama told him. "When you were born back in Belarus, we were so happy to have a child. It was cold and wet the night of your birth. The rain was leaking badly through the straw roof of our house. But right over the bed, there was no rain. God kept our bed dry all during the storm. We never felt as much as a drop.

"Then, when you were only one year old, just before we moved here, you got very sick. We thought you were going to die," Mama said softly. Her eyes filled with tears at the memory. But they were tears of joy as she continued gratefully, "Even then, God took care of you.

"You had such a high fever that I finally took you to the hospital. The doctor said I should just take you home. He said there was nothing he could do for you, and that you were going to die. It was cold, and you were hardly moving inside your blanket. All the way home I prayed earnestly to the Lord.

"As soon as I came into the house, I put you on the table and unwrapped your blanket. Pavel, you were cold, and your skin was turning blue. You were barely alive anymore, but I knelt on the floor. I told God that I believed He had work for you to do. With tears I begged Him to let you live. For a long time I prayed. Finally it seemed the Lord told me to get up off my knees. I got up, and there you were with warmth returning to your body again. Oh, how your papa and I praised God that night for healing you!"

Mama could say no more. She was wiping her eyes with the corner of her apron.

"*Da,*" Papa said, his voice full of emotion, "God surely did keep you here for a purpose."

"But we have no other children," Pavel said thoughtfully, looking at his parents.

"That is right," Papa replied. "Your mother had to have an operation after you were born. The doctor said she would not be able to have any more children. That is why we can have the big room in our house for the church."

Pavel looked at Papa. "Because our family is small?" he asked. He remembered the month they had spent with the cousins. It had seemed very strange to live with so many children.

"*Da,* my son. Most of the other families have many children. Since we have only you, we are thankful that we can provide room for the church services. At first we lived in that big room and later we built this part of the house we live in now," Papa explained.

Laying his hand on Pavel's head, he continued, "You must thank God for the special ways He has blessed you. Not only did He spare your life when you were a baby, but He has also given you the privilege of hearing the angels sing."

"I'm glad I heard the heavenly music," Pavel said with a smile. "It makes God seem even more real to me."

"Before we go to bed tonight," Papa said, "let's all pray together. Son, you are old enough to understand that if the reports are true, we may suffer hunger during the coming winter. I believe the reports are true. The tax collectors may come to Brothers' Village any day."

A shiver of fear ran down Pavel's back. He looked up into Papa's face with alarm. "What will we do?" he asked in a hoarse whisper.

"We will trust God," Papa said once again. "I will believe in God no matter what happens. I love Him too much to begin to doubt. I know that He loves us and that we are safe in that love."

The three of them knelt and Papa prayed first. He thanked God for the blessings they were receiving from Him. He thanked God for the good wheat harvest, for the cow, for Big Red, and for the chickens. He left almost nothing for Mama and Pavel to thank God for. Only at the end of the prayer did Papa clear his throat and say, "Please, God, I pray for wisdom. We need your help to know how to meet this new danger. We need you, Lord."

Pavel prayed next. "Thank you, God, for letting me hear the heavenly music. Thank you for sending that to me. I know it helps me to trust in you. Thank you for my parents and give Papa wisdom in this time."

When it was Mama's turn to pray, there was silence for a long time. At last she said in a shaky voice, "God, I do trust in you. I do thank you for all that you are doing for us. Please, God . . ." and then she couldn't pray anymore.

They were silent, but Pavel continued to pray in his mind. He knew that the threat was real. Somehow, though, he was not afraid tonight. Perhaps it was because he had heard the heavenly music. There was something different that he did not remember feeling before.

"The cow," Papa said after their prayer. "I hear God telling me to give the cow to Uncle Vladik. People from the other villages report that if any family has a little extra, the tax collectors take even more from them. We have both a horse and a cow. Maria, if you hear God saying the same thing, we will give the cow to my brother tomorrow."

Mama was silent for a moment and Pavel knew she was praying. When she lifted her head she said, "*Da,* Alexander, I agree with what God is telling you."

And just like that it was settled. The cow would go to Uncle Vladik. From now on Sasha or Andrei or Misha would have to take the cow to the grass.

That night as Pavel lay in bed, the darkness of fear about the tax collectors tried to come into his mind, but it could not. Pavel was remembering again the wonderful music he had heard. It had been so beautiful. He closed his eyes, and suddenly he thought he heard it again, soft and sweet. It was Mama, singing the song that Pavel had carefully copied for her.

> *Your voice, O Lord, is the voice I want to hear.*
> *Your will, O Lord, is the will of my heart.*

Only yours, Lord, only yours."

Da, the words were now in his dreams. The sweet sound of the music went on and on while Pavel slept. Slowly his worries melted away in the wonderful words of the song.

CHAPTER FIVE

The Tax Collectors Come

Big Red pulled the heavy millstone around and around over the wheat stalks on the barn floor. At first Pavel had to guide the horse, but after a while Big Red knew just where to go. On and on he walked around the circle all by himself.

The heavy stone crushed the bundles of wheat and separated the grain from the stalks. When the grain was all detached, they lifted the wheat straw and stacked it in the loft of the barn. In the winter they would use the straw as bedding for Big Red's stall and the hens' nesting boxes. They didn't need any straw for the cow anymore, for she was now in Uncle Vladik's barn.

Mama came out of the house and helped Papa and Pavel clean the wheat. The breeze was just right to blow away the chaff and dust as they tossed the wheat into the air. The heavy wheat fell right back down on the floor, but the light chaff drifted away in the breeze. Pavel swept the grain together and scooped it into a basket. Papa lifted the basket high and poured the wheat slowly into another basket to let the breeze carry away any last bits of straw or chaff.

Pavel helped carry the baskets into the granary and watched as Papa dumped them into a bin he had made especially for the wheat. The pile of wheat grew and grew. But oh, it was warm! Papa and Mama and Pavel were all wet with sweat.

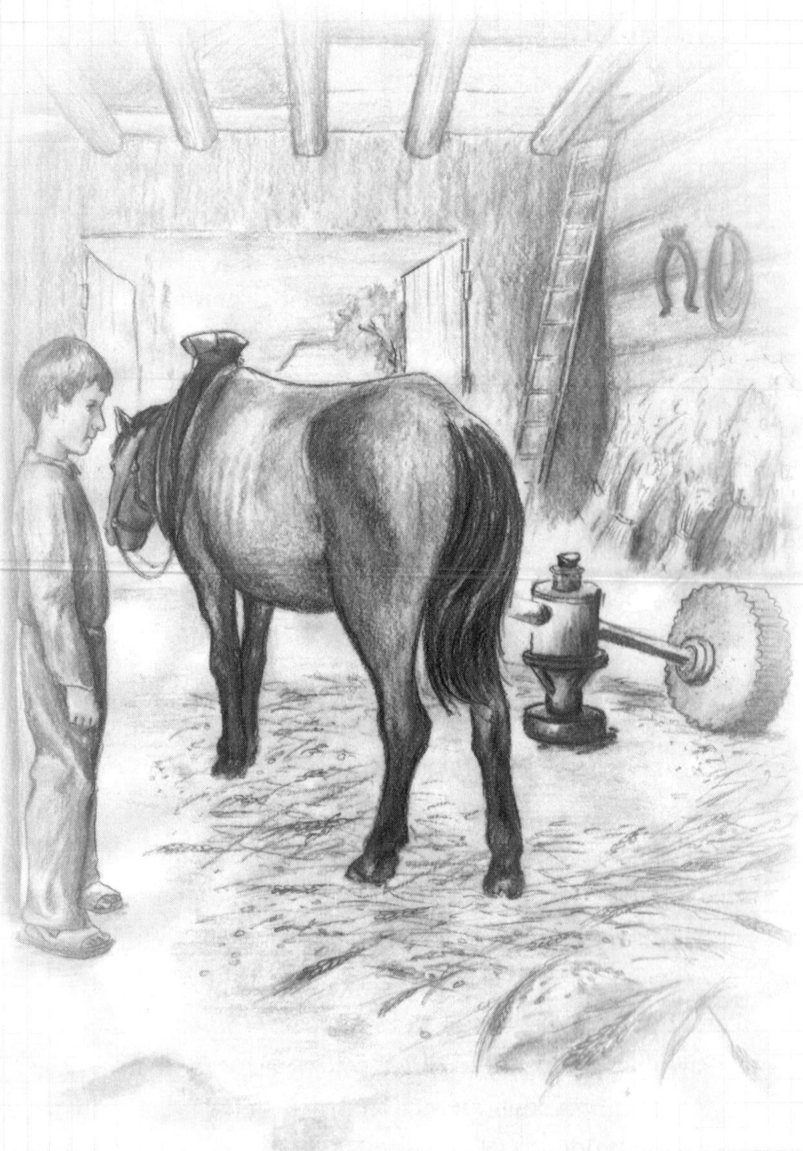

Papa wiped his forehead with a handkerchief. "My hand-kerchief is as wet as my forehead, so I just spread the sweat around instead of drying it," Papa laughed. His shirt was wet all the way through as well.

Out on the street the sound of a truck was coming closer. Pavel tried to see it through the barn window, but he was too short. The roar of the engine grew louder, and then they heard the screech of brakes. The engine stopped somewhere nearby. It was unusual for a truck to come to Brothers' Village. Some-times a truck delivered some building materials, but the ar-rival of any vehicle was always a big event.

Papa did not try to look out at the truck. He glanced at Mama, and just for a moment, he bowed his head. Then he calmly continued to sweep the barn floor.

Pavel wanted to run out and see what was happening on the street. Another part of him wanted to ask Papa and Mama what was happening and why they looked so sober. But he did neither. He did not ask any questions. He continued to help his parents with the wheat. The late summer day made him hot and thirsty, but he did not even go to the water pail in the kitchen to get water. He just worked.

The small barn with its tools was the same barn he had al-ways known. Right now, though, it seemed like a very special place to Pavel. The barn had never seemed such a safe haven before. It had a secure stall for the horse and nests for the chickens. Most of all, it had a grain bin for the wheat. The scythe hung safely on the wall along with the rakes. Papa was using the broom to sweep the barn floor. To Pavel, all those things suddenly seemed very important. He tried to ignore the loud voices in the street. Papa and Mama did not speak, but they continued to work. Mama kept her face hidden.

The village dogs were barking and there was a lot of noise all that Saturday afternoon. The hot sun continued to shine and everyone was sweating. At last the little family was finished with their work. The wheat was all in the bin, and the bin was nearly full. Papa had made a wooden cover especially to keep the wheat clean. The lid banged loudly as it slammed down and the grain bin was safely closed. It would be too bad to have any of the animals eat the wheat if they got loose. The wheat had to be protected.

Then the noise that they had been hearing came right into their yard. The truck's engine roared again and this time it pulled up in front of the barn. The motor stopped and the men on the back of the truck jumped off. The driver climbed down from the cab.

Papa, Mama, and Pavel stood silently in the doorway of the barn. They watched the truck come, and they watched the men jump off the truck. The back of the truck was full of bags. The bags looked as if they held wheat.

The driver of the truck looked about the yard. He noted the house that was bigger than other houses in the village. He looked at Big Red, who was watching the strange truck suspiciously. Finally the man looked at the three silent people in the doorway of the barn.

"You are a rich family," he said, nodding his head. "You have plenty to share with the people of our great motherland. Russia is proud to have people like you with wealth and food to share with your comrades."

The driver walked boldly into the barn. He looked at the

hand tools on the wall. He reached up and pulled down some of the wheat straw from the loft above him. Then he noticed the grain bin and walked over to it. With a mighty shove, he threw aside the wooden cover.

"Ah," he said with satisfaction. He reached down and plunged his arm deep into the pile of wheat. "Bring the bags," he ordered the men who were standing at the back of the truck.

Two of the men brought a stack of empty bags to the driver. Two more brought large scoops and the five men set to work. With their scoops the men began to shovel up the wheat and pour it into their bags.

Pavel watched the men's arms go up and down as they scooped up the wheat. They poured it into the bags and then reached down deep inside the bin to get more. The wheat poured in golden streams out of the scoops and into the bags. As soon as a bag was filled, one of the men tied the top with a bit of twine and set it on the other side of the barn.

The sun shone hot and Pavel could see that the shirts of the men were all wet. They had been working in the heat all afternoon, and their faces were red and sweaty. None of them bothered to use the handkerchiefs that hung from their back pockets. They were so soaked and limp that they could not have wiped any more sweat from their faces.

Papa and Mama stood quietly beside Pavel. They said nothing.

The barn was quiet except for the sound of the working men. The muffled noise of the wheat pouring into bags made a soft swish. As the bags filled up, the sound became shorter and deeper.

It seemed to Pavel that inside him there was a sound louder

than the wheat. He actually thought the men might hear it. Yet it was not even a real sound. It was the sound of silent screaming in his mind.

Fifteen bags. Pavel counted fifteen bags of wheat, all standing in neat rows along the wall. The men continued working.

Papa said something to Mama in a low, calm voice. A moment later he left the barn with Mama following him. They did not say anything to Pavel.

Pavel continued to stare. He wanted to leave, but his feet would not move. He no longer even wanted to count the bags. Somehow, though, his eyes continued to count every time another one was added. There were now nineteen bags of the wheat they had worked so hard to plant, raise, and harvest. Nineteen bags of wheat that would have made bread for the winter. Now all that wheat would simply be carried away by the communist government workers.

"You are very warm," Papa's voice said suddenly beside Pavel. "Look, I have brought water for you to drink. Also, we have been blessed by God with a good watermelon crop. I have brought up a big melon from the cool shade. I will cut it open so you can enjoy it. It will taste refreshing on a hot day like this."

Pavel looked at Papa, surprised. *Da,* he really was giving water to the men who were taking away their wheat. He gave them glass after glass of water. They drank thirstily and several of them asked for more.

By now Mama had brought the knife to cut the watermelon. She had a tray of bread too.

Papa knelt on the barn floor. Before he cut the watermelon,

he prayed right in front of the men who were taking the wheat they needed for the winter. It wasn't any special prayer, just thanking God for His goodness and kindness. Papa thanked God for the harvest. He thanked Him for Jesus. He thanked Him for the change He brought into the lives of all who believed on Him. The prayer was really just like all the ones they prayed before eating.

Then Papa cut the watermelon. The dark red inside looked cool and refreshing on such a hot day. Again and again he cut, slicing that big, juicy watermelon into pieces.

The men all stopped working and watched Papa. The driver stood with a bag of wheat in his hands, ready to tie it. That would be bag number twenty. Pavel knew because he was still counting.

The men watched silently as the knife cut that cool watermelon into slices. They watched Papa as he laid the knife down. They continued to stare silently as he stood up to hand the watermelon to the hot, sweaty men.

One man began to reach for a piece of watermelon when the driver suddenly cleared his throat. The man jerked his hand back and looked uncertainly at the driver.

"Take it," Papa said in his usual calm voice. "It will cool you off, and we are happy to share." He offered a slice to the driver.

Pavel could see it all plainly. Papa stood there, his hand stretched out toward the driver, offering a beautiful watermelon slice.

The driver's eyes took in the scene—the watermelon, the knife, the sober but calm family. He cast a sidelong glance at his men, who were not looking at him. Several were awk-

wardly studying the barn floor. One was looking out the door at the truck with wheat bags on the back.

"Thank you," Pavel heard at last. The driver had decided to accept the watermelon. Mama helped Papa pass out the other watermelon slices.

The men ate hungrily. They wolfed down the bread Mama gave to them. They devoured the entire watermelon and the whole loaf of bread.

The driver wiped his sweaty forehead with the sleeve of his wet shirt. He looked into the bin where wheat was still scattered on the bottom. He looked at the empty bags on the floor and at the twenty full bags stacked along the wall.

Several of the men were leaning against the walls of the barn. Pavel noticed their sagging shoulders. They had worked hard that day.

The green watermelon rinds were piled on the floor, the red part all gone. The driver looked at the rinds. "We will come back next week," he said finally. "We have enough on the truck for this week." He looked at the wheat left in the bin, and then he glanced once more at the twenty bags of wheat on the barn floor.

Several of the men began to pick up the bagged wheat, but the driver stopped them. "Leave the wheat. We can get that next week." He motioned with his head toward the truck. The men who were bending over the bags straightened their backs and looked at him in surprise.

But the driver said nothing. He was already walking out of the barn, empty-handed. With a nod toward Papa and Mama, he climbed into the cab and started the engine. The other workers jumped on the back of the truck and left with a roar of the engine and grinding of gears.

All was very quiet after the truck had gone. Papa looked at Mama and Mama looked at the floor. Pavel looked at the twenty bags of wheat.

Papa walked over to the wheat bin. Bending over, he lifted the cover and gazed into the yawning hole. Then, straightening, he let the cover fall into its place with a *bang*. "Pavel, take Big Red out to the grass," Papa said just as he would have on any ordinary day.

That evening after their supper, Papa sat on the bench outside with Mama beside him. Pavel wanted to sit with them, but they were talking in low voices. Pavel wasn't sure if he was supposed to hear them. Then Papa called out, "Come, my boy, sit with us."

Pavel settled beside Papa.

"Tonight your story will be about Job," Papa began. "Pavel, you know the story, and Mama and I know the story, but we all need to hear it again."

Pavel nodded. *Da*, he knew the story. But his thoughts kept returning to the wheat—those twenty bags and the little pile left in the grain bin. He wanted to think about the winter and about grinding wheat to make flour and about the crusty loaves of nourishing bread. Would it be like Belarus again with no bread to eat?

"Job was a man who loved God very much," Papa said. "He always wanted to do everything he could to please God. Even after his children were grown, Job still prayed for them every day. Oh, did I tell you that he was an extremely rich man? He was so rich, it is hard to imagine. He had camels and sheep and goats and fields and barns full of feed for the cattle and food for himself and his family," Papa said.

"Did he have wheat too?" Pavel could not help it. He just had to ask.

Papa put his strong arm around Pavel's shoulder, and it felt warm and comforting. "I think he probably did, Pavlik," he replied softly.

Then he continued, "One day Job saw a messenger coming. The messenger told him that his cattle had been stolen. Another servant came and told him his sheep had been destroyed. More messengers kept coming and telling him that all his riches were being lost or destroyed. Last of all, someone came and told him all his children had been killed.

"So much bad news all in one day was very hard for Job. Of course he felt sad, but he said, 'The Lord has given all these things and the Lord has taken them away.' "

"Was it really the Lord who took them away?" Pavel asked. "Why would God do such an awful thing?"

"Ah, that is a good question," Papa replied. "There was one thing Job did not know. He did not know that Satan had come to the Lord and spoken about Job. He did not know that God had allowed Satan to destroy all his belongings. He even gave Satan permission to take away Job's family. But Job did not know that it was not God who had done all this. It was Satan."

"But the Lord allowed Satan to do all that," Pavel mused. He could not help but wonder why this was so.

"*Da*, son. We do not understand all the ways of the Lord. Even so, in our story, Job was a wonderful example for us.

He really thought it was God who did this to him. Later he got very sick, but Job did one thing that was very good. He determined that even if he lost his life, he would still believe and trust in God. That is the lesson we need to learn from Job," Papa said.

There was silence for a few moments. "We always want to know how things will turn out," Mama said quietly. "The waiting is the hard part."

"*Da*," Papa agreed. "That is when our faith in God must be strong."

It was hard for Pavel to think. One part of him wanted to believe that God would take care of them. Another part of him wondered how God would do it. How could He possibly feed them if the wheat was gone? And the people from the village were saying that not only wheat but also other crops were being taken. To Pavel, the other crops were not so important. Only the wheat mattered, because wheat meant bread. He could not imagine a winter without bread.

"Remember the singing and the music you heard?" Papa was saying. "Pavel, God let you hear that not only for yourself, but also for us and for all the believers in our village. I have told your story to the church, and many of us are praising God. Even though such great trouble is coming to our village, we know that God has not changed. The music you heard is God's way of reminding us that He has not forgotten us."

Pavel did not feel proud. He felt happy, but he knew he had not done anything special. It was only because God wanted to encourage the village through the singing he had heard. They all needed to be reminded that God had not forgotten them.

As he lay in bed that night after they had prayed, Pavel heard Mama singing again. Softly, she sang to herself.

> *"Your will, O Lord, is the will of my heart.*
> *Only yours, Lord, only yours."*

Once more Pavel fell asleep, the words of the song becoming a part of his dream. He forgot about the wheat and slept peacefully.

CHAPTER SIX

Twenty Bags of Wheat

When Pavel went to feed the chickens and gather the eggs the next morning, the twenty bags of wheat were still there. He counted them. He wanted to lift the wooden cover from the grain bin and see how much wheat was left, but he couldn't move the heavy lid. He remembered that before Papa had replaced the cover, he had seen the wooden boards at the bottom of the bin. That meant not very much wheat was left in the bin. He tried to imagine how the bin would look when the men returned and took all the wheat.

On Monday when Pavel returned from school, he went to the barn and counted the bags again. There were still twenty. He thought about what the children had said in school. Not out loud, but in fearful whispers, they had told of their loss.

"They took all our wheat," one girl said, her eyes big and sober.

"They took our horse," an older boy said, and Pavel thought about Big Red.

"I heard an uncle say that they will take the men and make them work on government projects," said a girl with brown braids. "They already took men from the village nearby."

Pavel did not talk about the wheat in their barn. He did not tell the children that Papa and Mama had given the tax people watermelon and bread. He said nothing.

One day Pavel was walking home from school with his cousins. After they reached Uncle Vladik's house, Pavel walked on by himself. As he glanced at the stones on the familiar road, a memory struck him. The music! It was here that he had heard the heavenly singing! He stopped and listened, but today the heavens were silent. There were the usual village noises—the voices of men in the fields and of children in the yards—but no singing. Even the village noise seemed quiet and subdued. There was a heavy feeling in the air like clouds hanging low. Pavel shivered in spite of the warm sunshine and hurried home.

"Take this bread with you," Mama offered Pavel as he prepared to take Big Red to the grass. "You must be hungry after a long day at school."

Pavel eagerly stuffed the bread into his big pocket. He was glad that Mama had put big pockets in his trousers. They were perfect for carrying things like bread. Again he stopped to check on the bags of wheat in the barn. All twenty bags were still lined up silently beside the wall, waiting. Pavel tugged on Big Red's rope and led him down the road toward the end of the village near the railroad tracks.

The grass along the tracks was not very good for Big Red to eat. However, the grass along the ditch was good and green. The rainwater that collected in the ditch made the grass grow well there. Big Red eagerly chomped big mouthfuls of it. Pavel sat on the side of the ditch with his chin on his knees and thought.

Far off in the distance he heard the rumble of the train. Quickly he jumped up and pulled Big Red away from the train tracks. Even though the train went past Brothers' Village every day, Big Red did not like the noise it made. He always tried to run back home when the locomotive went rushing past. Pavel did not like to run after his scared horse, so he led Big Red away from the tracks before the train got there.

Even at a safe distance, Big Red danced nervously from one foot to the other and held his head high. The skin of his reddish-brown neck shivered.

Pavel spoke soothingly to the horse, trying to calm him. "Big Red, the train won't get you so far back from the tracks. You don't have to be afraid because I'm looking after you. Even though you don't understand now, perhaps someday you will when you become a man." As he spoke the words, he began to smile at the absurd idea of saying that to a horse. But the near smile faded as he again felt a heaviness in his heart. He did not feel like laughing at his joke.

After the train had passed, Pavel took Big Red back to eat the good grass on the sides of the ditch. Soon Pavel saw two children coming slowly toward him, walking on the train tracks. As they came closer, he could see that the bigger child was a girl, perhaps his own age. A little boy, about five years old, stumbled along beside her.

Pavel had never seen them before and thought they must live in the next village. The girl, who was carrying a small bag, looked hungry and thin. As the boy dragged himself along beside her, hopeless tears trailed silently down his cheeks. The girl glanced at Pavel and Big Red but quickly looked away again. She pulled on the boy's hand, trying to hurry him along.

The children were right beside Pavel now. He could feel their sadness, and his heart went out to them. He thrust his hand into his pocket, feeling the bread. The children passed him as they went on down the track.

"Wait," Pavel heard his voice call suddenly. The children stopped and turned to look at him. They said nothing.

Pavel pulled the big chunk of bread out of his pocket. He walked toward them, holding it out. The girl looked at the bread and then back at him. She shook her head.

"Please take it," Pavel said. "I don't need it."

The boy needed no more persuasion. His hand shot out and took the piece. He stuffed a big bite into his mouth. His crying stopped because his mouth was so full of Mama's good bread.

The girl smiled and said "Thank you" in a small voice. Then the children left. Once, when the girl looked back at Pavel, she had bread in her mouth and was chewing rapidly.

Pavel went back to where he had been sitting. He took a stick and began poking it into the ground, thinking of the hungry children. He listened to the sound of Big Red cutting the grass with his sharp teeth.

That evening Mama put the food on the table. There was bread, big slices of it, and *vareneki* (vah REH nee kee), which is boiled dough filled with pieces of carrots and cabbage. Pavel liked *vareneki,* and he ate his portion enthusiastically.

"I have been thinking," Mama said while they ate, "that maybe we don't need to keep so much food around. To prepare for the winter," she finished, looking at Papa.

Papa understood. Mama was thinking of the wheat and of the men who were coming that week to take it away. She was thinking they should share it with their friends before the tax people took it all.

Pavel stopped eating. The last of his *vareneki* waited on his plate, but he left it there. What would Papa say?

As soon as Papa spoke, Pavel put the *vareneki* in his mouth. Of course, he should have known what Papa would say. Papa always said it when there was a decision to make. "We will ask God what we should do," he stated.

Papa left after supper and was gone for a long time. Pavel did not want to go to bed before Papa returned, so he wandered out to the barn in the fading light. As usual, he found himself counting the bags of wheat, but this time there were only nineteen! One bag was missing!

Pavel remembered his parents' conversation at supper. He walked silently back to the bench under the grape arbor and sat down. Mama did not say anything about it being Pavel's bedtime. She was working in the kitchen, and Pavel was sitting on the bench outside, just waiting.

Finally, in the darkness, Pavel heard footsteps and knew they were Papa's. No one else walked just like his father.

"You are still sitting here, my son," Papa said. He sat down on the bench beside Pavel. Mama heard his voice and came outside to join them.

"You were right, Maria," Papa said softly. "Aunt Nina did need that wheat. Her children were hungry. *Da,* I believe God is telling me that we need to make our meals smaller. Not just so that we will have food for the winter, but so that we will have food to share with others."

Pavel knew Aunt Nina. Of course, he knew everyone in the village. All the villagers knew each other, and many of them were related. He thought about Aunt Nina's two small children. They had no papa, for Aunt Nina's husband had died two years earlier. Pavel had only been six then, but he remembered how sad Aunt Nina had looked at the funeral.

So that was where the one bag of wheat had gone—to help Aunt Nina and her children.

Pavel felt like a voice was shouting in his head. It seemed to be saying, "No, no! Don't give away our wheat! We are going to need it for the winter." Another voice asked whether they should give away the wheat if the tax men said it now belonged to the government. Still another quiet voice told him that it was better for Aunt Nina and her children to have the wheat than for the government to get it and waste it.

There were too many confusing voices inside him. Pavel put his head down and began to cry. Papa put his hand on Pavel's head and smoothed his hair comfortingly. He said nothing for a while. Finally he began to speak in a gentle voice. "It is good for us to prepare for the days that are coming," he said. "God gave us the harvest so we could prepare and put away food for the winter. It has always been so.

"But we must not be like the rich man in the Bible story. That man had his barns full and still there was more harvest. So he decided he would build bigger barns that could hold all his crops. But God called him foolish. That rich man forgot that he would die someday and all his harvest would do him no good. That very same night, after making plans to build more barns, he died. The rich man had forgotten that there is something more important than having food. That important thing is to have Jesus living in our hearts. Then even our concern about food becomes less important. Do you think you understand, Pavlik? We must make preparation for our souls because they live forever. Food does not last forever. Anyway, we can never store up enough food to last us forever. We must trust that God will provide. He always does."

Pavel said nothing, but he was thinking, *"But what if they take all the wheat? Then what will we eat this winter?"*

Mama spoke softly. "God has reminded me of how He sent the ravens to feed Elijah. Do you remember the story, Pavel?"

Pavel nodded his head. *Da,* he always thought of that story when he saw the big black ravens in their village. He pictured how strange it would be to have the ravens bring food, especially bread. In Brothers' Village, the ravens were always trying to steal any food they could.

"When God wants us to know His power, anything can happen," Papa said confidently. "When He puts His Spirit in our hearts, we can do things we thought were impossible."

Suddenly Pavel remembered the bread he had given to the children. He wondered if God had given him the strength to do that. He had wanted to eat the bread himself. He said nothing, though, because he didn't want to sound as if he were boasting.

"Did you ever wonder how it was possible for David to kill the lion and the bear that tried to catch his sheep?" Papa asked.

Pavel knew that story from the Bible well. "I suppose David must have been a very strong man," he said thoughtfully.

"Oh, no, David was not strong enough to do it by himself. It was the Spirit of the Lord who came on David and gave him such strength. That same Spirit of the Lord can come on any believer and give him strength to do things he could not do by himself."

It was a big truth for a young boy, but Pavel thought he understood it. He was not to worry about how they would manage without the wheat because God would do something amazing for them.

That night Pavel lay in his bed, but he was not sleeping. He was listening to Mama sing the new song. He was also hearing something else in his mind. He was remembering his own words to Big Red when the train was coming. "You do not need to be afraid, for I will look after you."

It seemed to Pavel that those were not only his words to Big Red. They were also the words from heaven. God was saying the same thing to his heart. As Mama continued singing, the dark clouds lifted. Once more the words of the song seemed to carry Pavel off to sweet dreams.

CHAPTER SEVEN

The Tax Collectors Return

Six days had passed. The tax collectors had not yet come for the wheat. The bags were still stacked against the wall of the barn. Every afternoon when Pavel returned from school, he counted the bags. Nineteen.

"Pavlik, I want you to help me with something," Papa said on the seventh day. "Come, my son."

Pavel wondered what job Papa needed his help for. Would they work in the vegetable garden? Would they go and gather some of the hay that Papa had cut for Big Red to eat in the winter?

Papa walked to the barn with Pavel trotting beside him. He lifted the empty bag that had held Aunt Nina's wheat. It was one of the bags the men had brought from the back of the truck. Since it was not their own bag, Mama had brought it back and put it with the other nineteen full bags. Pavel wondered what the tax men would say about the empty bag.

"Hold the bag just like this," Papa instructed. While Pavel held it, Papa opened the heavy lid of the grain bin. He reached down deep into the bin with the big scoop. He filled the scoop, then turned and poured it into the empty bag Pavel was holding. The golden grains of wheat made a rushing sound as they hit the bottom of the bag.

Pavel looked at Papa. Papa smiled encouragingly at him and turned to get another scoop of wheat. Once more he emptied it into the bag. Again and again he scooped and poured until the bag was full.

Pavel's mind was spinning, but he did not say anything. He heard how the scoop scraped the bottom of the bin. When the bag was full and Papa was tying it, Pavel climbed up and peered into the bin. The scattered wheat at the bottom made a pitiful little pile. Pavel remembered the many hours of hard work that had gone into planting, weeding, and harvesting the wheat. Had they done all that work for this little bit of wheat? How could it possibly feed them through the long winter?

"Mama and I want twenty bags to be waiting for the men when they come back with the truck," Papa said. "God has told us to let them have all twenty bags that they have claimed. We will not try to keep even one bag from them."

Pavel nodded. He understood. God could do even more than Papa could. God would not want them to hide the wheat or take it away. They were to trust in God.

That afternoon the tax men returned.

Pavel had not yet taken Big Red out to eat the grass. Neither had he taken their horse away and hidden him like some of the men from the village had suggested. No, Big Red was right there when the men returned. Papa and Mama and Pavel were there too.

Papa was in the barn mending Big Red's harness. Mama was taking loaves of bread out of the hot clay oven in the back yard. Pavel was putting new straw in the hens' nests.

When he heard the roar of the truck's motor, Pavel knew immediately what it was. He stood up and went to the barn to stand beside Papa. Mama came to the door of the house and watched silently from the doorway. The truck rattled to a stop in the yard and the driver climbed out. Another man hopped down from the other side of the cab. The back of the truck was empty.

When the men saw Papa standing in the barn beside his son, they nodded toward him in a friendly way. "Good afternoon," they said.

Papa nodded his head and pleasantly replied, "Good afternoon," as if he were greeting a friend who had come to visit.

The driver was the same man who had been there before, bagging their wheat. Pavel recognized the other man as one of the workers who had eaten their watermelon.

They walked over to the wheat bags. Pavel watched as they counted with their eyes. Twenty bags, just as they had left them. The driver untied the string from the mouth of the first bag. He motioned silently with his head and the other man walked over to the grain bin and removed the heavy cover. The driver picked up his bag and tipped it over the side of the bin. With a rushing sound, he poured the wheat back into the bin. Then he put the empty bag on the floor!

Pavel was so surprised that his mouth dropped open. He looked at Papa, and Pavel could see surprise on his face as well. He stared back at the men.

One by one they were opening the sacks of wheat they had bagged the week before. One by one they were emptying them back into the grain bin!

Pavel's mind was racing with questions. Were the men really giving some of the wheat back? Would they bag it again later and take it away? Why were they doing this?

No one said a word. The men just walked back and forth, opening the bags, carrying them to the grain bin, and tipping the wheat into the bin in a golden shower.

They did not stop until all twenty bags of wheat were poured back into the bin. Then they silently replaced the wooden cover and picked up their empty bags. With friendly smiles, they nodded at Papa and went back to the truck. The driver started the engine as the other man jumped in beside him. They waved as the truck roared away from the village.

Mama came to stand beside Papa. She shakily reached out and touched his sleeve. Papa had his head bowed and his eyes closed. Without opening his eyes, he put his arm around Mama and pulled her close to him. His other arm found Pavel and pulled him into the little circle.

Papa began to pray. They all prayed. This time they didn't even wait to take turns. All three of them just let the words of praise come bubbling up out of their hearts. It seemed they just could not get finished praising and thanking God. Pavel knew that Mama was crying tears of happiness, and he heard tears in Papa's voice also. Pavel's own eyes were wet as he felt a great fountain of joy come swelling from his heart.

The wheat was saved! God had somehow changed the hearts of the tax men, and they had returned the wheat to the bin.

That evening after supper there was no story about what had happened in the past, no story of what God had done a long time ago. All the talk was about what God had done that very day.

"God softened the hearts of those men," Papa said reflectively as the evening light shone faintly in on them from the

western sky. "They returned all the wheat to us."

"Was it because we gave them the watermelon? And bread?" Pavel asked.

Papa was silent for a moment. "How do I answer, Pavlik?" he replied at last. "See if this truth is something you can understand. When the men were here last week, we were watching them bag the wheat. I was asking God to show me how to bear this trouble. Then I heard God say to me, 'Feed them.'

"I understood immediately. The Bible teaches us to do good to those who harm us. It says that when we return good for evil, we are heaping coals of fire on the heads of our enemies. This time, it was more than just knowing the teaching. From deep in my heart, I felt that I truly wanted to bless those men and share our food with them. That is why I gave them watermelon and bread. I heard God asking me to do it, and I truly wanted to obey Him. I was happy to share with those tax men.

"No, I did not know that they would return and give the wheat back. But I did believe that God would provide for us if I obeyed Him. I did not know how God would provide, but I did trust Him. This trust was not from me, but God put it into my heart. Do you understand, son?"

"*Da*, Papa," Pavel said thoughtfully. He knew that he had seen something wonderful that day. It was something he would never forget as long as he lived.

He knew now that he did not need a bin full of wheat to trust that God would take care of him. The wheat for the bread was good, but there was something that spoke to his heart more deeply. Trusting in God was the most important thing of all, far better than having plenty of food.

"If we do not feed the wheat to the chickens or to Big Red, we will have enough to share with the families in the village," Mama said. "I know God has not spared the wheat just for us. He expects us to share with the others as long as it lasts. We will find other ways to feed the animals."

Pavel nodded his head. He understood, and he was not afraid. *Da,* they would share, and God would take care of the rest. That was all that mattered. As the family knelt to pray again before going to bed, their hearts were still full of praise and thanksgiving to their great God.

Once more night covered the little Ukrainian village. The lights in the houses were going out, and Brothers' Village was quiet and peaceful. In his bed, Pavel drifted into a sound sleep. The heavenly music came back again in his dreams. He smiled in his sleep, for in his dream he had joined the singing chorus as they delighted in praising the God who provides.

About the Author

Harvey Yoder and his wife Karen live in the beautiful mountains of western North Carolina. They have five children, all of whom are married, as well as eight grandchildren. A teacher for many years, Harvey is now a licensed real estate agent in addition to being a prolific writer. He has traveled extensively while gathering materials for his many books, most of which have been published by Christian Aid Ministries. Harvey finds it especially fulfilling to write the inspiring accounts of faithful believers whose stories would otherwise remain unknown. His greatest desire in writing is that his readers will not merely be entertained by the stories, but rather be motivated to seek God with all their hearts.